More Maths Challeng

Graded problems for 9–12 year-olds

Anne Joshua

STANLEY
THORNES

Copyright © Longman Cheshire 1991

First published in 1991 by
Longman Cheshire Pty Limited, Australia

Reprinted in 1994 by Simon & Schuster Education

This edition published exclusively for W H Smith 1997 by
Stanley Thornes (Publishers) Ltd
Ellenborough House
Wellington Street
Cheltenham
GL50 1YW

97 98 99 00 01 \ 10 9 8 7 6 5 4 3 2 1

Designed by Norma van Rees
Illustrations by Boris Silvestri
Set in Plantin Light 12½/14½pt.
Printed in Great Britain by The Baskerville Press, Salisbury, Wiltshire

A catalogue record of this book is available from the British Library

ISBN 0-7487-3404-X

Contents

Introduction

This series of eight books will help to stimulate and challenge your child to think and develop mathematically, enabling them to relate mathematics to everyday life and to think logically and more strategically.

The activities, which all support National Curriculum mathematics and are excellent examples of good practice in mathematics, are graded to allow you to observe and participate in your child's development. The activities are lively and will really get your child thinking.

Here are some practical suggestion on how you can help:

- Ensure your child understands the question.

- Where do I start? Beginning is often a block for children; encourage them, pretend to be a detective and see what clues you have already.

- Encourage your child to have the confidence to have a go.

- In some of the activities there could be several solutions; let your child know that there may be many ways to solve the question.

- Can you find a pattern? Asking your child if he/she can see any common features is a major step in mathematical thinking. Once children begin to see and explore patterns, they gain confidence and are often able to use the information gathered again in a new situation.

- Let's get organised! Encourage your child to put thoughts on paper, firstly so that he/she can make sense of them and, then, so that others are able to understand the notes he/she makes. This is an important aspect of mathematics. This may need some help from you. Show your child how you would set the information out: it will give clues and demonstrate the need to be systematic. Getting organised is one aspect of mathematics which will take time ... it requires patience and understanding.

- Can you find a rule? Many of the activities in the books will encourage your child to find a rule and check whether the rule works in all cases. Encourage your child to reflect on the problem he/she has solved and to discuss what he/she has learnt from it.

- Keep a record of your child's work and look back on the progress he/she has made.

Problem solving: Guess and check

1 Arrange the numbers from 1 to 7 in the circles of each figure so that the sum along each line is the number given below the figure.

(a)

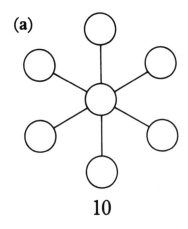

10

(b)

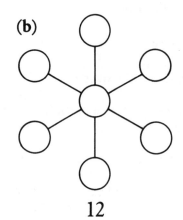

12

(c)

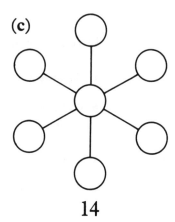

14

Hint: Try 1 in the centre.

2 Arrange the numbers from 1 to 9 in the circles of each figure so that the sum along each line is the number given below the figure.

(a)

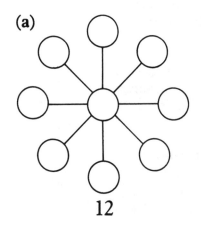

12

(b)

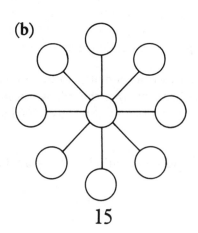

15

(c)

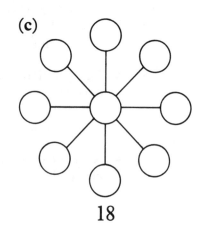

18

Hint: Try 1 in the centre.

3 Can you arrange the numbers so that other totals can be made? Explain.

What is my message?

In these messages, the letters have been replaced with numbers. Discover what they say, using the set of problems below each one as a key to the code.

1 $\overline{1\,8\,3\,5\,5}$ ' $\overline{7}$ $\overline{1\,8\,2\,2}$ $\overline{4\,0}$ $\overline{6\,9\,7}$

$L \times L = L + L$	$C + L = K$	$K \div K = R$
$R \times R = R$	$C^2 = U$	$L \times S = S$
$R + R = L$	$L^2 = I$	$N \times K = CK$
$C - L = R$	$L \times I = O$	$IU \div N = N$
$C \times L = F$	$F - F = S$	

2 $\overline{4\,9\,1\,8\,7}$ $\overline{3\,7}$ $\overline{6\,2\,5\,5\,6}$

$M \div M = T$	$Y \times Y = IY$
$T \times T = T$	$T + U = I$
$I^2 = A$	$A - K = M$
$U^2 = M$	$MK \div K = A$
$K \times K = UK$	$IU \div H = M$

$$\begin{array}{r} THIS \\ IS + \\ \hline THSM \end{array} \qquad \begin{array}{r} AM \\ AM \\ AM + \\ \hline UHU \end{array}$$

3 Try to make up your own coded message.

Missing numbers

All these exercises follow the same rule.

First find the rule by working through exercises 1 and 2.

1 4 → □ → 12 → ○ → 24 → △ → 14 → ◇ → 7

2 7 → □ → 15 → ○ → 30 → △ → 20 → ◇ → 10

Using this rule, find the missing numbers in exercises 3 to 12.

3 9 → □ → __ → ○ → __ → △ → __ → ◇ → 12

4 10 → □ → __ → ○ → __ → △ → __ → ◇ → __

5 12 → □ → __ → ○ → __ → △ → __ → ◇ → __

6 __ → □ → 13 → ○ → __ → △ → __ → ◇ → __

7 __ → □ → __ → ○ → 18 → △ → __ → ◇ → __

8 __ → □ → __ → ○ → __ → △ → 50 → ◇ → __

9 __ → □ → __ → ○ → __ → △ → 42 → ◇ → __

10 __ → □ → __ → ○ → __ → △ → 36 → ◇ → __

11 __ → □ → __ → ○ → __ → △ → __ → ◇ → 20

12 __ → □ → __ → ○ → __ → △ → __ → ◇ → 32

Number squares

Find the values of the letters A, B, C, D and E in these squares. The sum of each row and column is given, and only the numbers 1, 2, 3, 4, 5 and 6 have been used. Starting with the one letter-value given for each square, you will be able to work out the others.

1

D	A	C	12
E	C	D	11
B	D	E	8
8	12	11	

A B C D E
              2

Hint: Only the numbers 1, 2, 3, 4 and 5 have been used in this square.

			12
2			11
		2	8
8	12	11	

2

D	A	E	6
B	C	E	11
A	D	B	8
8	9	8	

A B C D E
1

	1		6
			11
1			8
8	9	8	

3

E	B	A	12
D	A	C	6
C	E	D	7
7	12	6	

A B C D E
3

		3	12
	3		6
			7
7	12	6	

4

A	D	E	9
F	B	C	12
E	F	B	9
12	7	11	

A B C D E F
5

5			9
			12
			9
12	7	11	

5

D	C	A	10
A	B	E	9
B	A	F	10
11	6	12	

A B C D E F
               4

			10
		4	9
			10
11	6	12	

Completing the lines

1 Can you make these squares, in which some numbers are missing, into magic squares? Work out which numbers you must put in the empty boxes so that all lines — horizontal, vertical and diagonal — will have the same total. You must first find each magic sum.

(a)

			10
14	9	8	3
12		2	
1	4		

(b)

8		2	
	5		3
	4	9	
1		7	12

(c)

8	15		5
	11		4
	6	7	
	10	3	

(d)

33	5		27
11		21	
	15		
9	29		3

(e)

23		10	20
12	18		
16	14	13	
11			

2 Complete each square grid below so that one — *and only one* — of the digits 1, 2, 3, 4 and 5 appears in each row, column or diagonal line.

(a)

1	3	5	2	4
5	2			
4	1			
3				

(b)

1	2	3	4	5
3	4	5		
5	1			

Largest and smallest

In these number sentences, □ is a one-digit number (such as 5 or 6), while □□ is a two-digit number (such as 34 or 78).

Choosing any of the digits 1, 2, 3, 4, 5, 6, 7, 8 and 9, and using each one only *once* in a number sentence, fill in the small squares and complete the sentences so that:

1 You have the *largest* possible answer.

(a) □ + □ =
(b) □ + □ + □ =
(c) □ + □ + □ + □ =
(d) □ − □ =
(e) □ + □ − □ =
(f) □ − □ − □ =
(g) □□ =
(h) □□ + □ =
(i) □□ − □ =
(j) □□ + □□ =
(k) □□ − □□ =
(l) □□ − □□ − □ =

2 You have the *smallest* possible answer (positive or zero).

(a) □ + □ =
(b) □ + □ + □ =
(c) □ + □ + □ + □ =
(d) □ − □ =
(e) □ + □ − □ =
(f) □ − □ − □ =
(g) □□ =
(h) □□ + □ =
(i) □□ − □ =
(j) □□ + □□ =
(k) □□ − □□ =
(l) □□ − □□ − □ =

There are several possible solutions to some parts of group 2. Can you find them all? Why are there several solutions to some of them?

Remember to work systematically and also to use a digit only once in each sentence.

Multiplying puzzles

Try using a calculator to work out these problems. In each one, a digit can be used *once* only.

1 Using the digits 1, 2, 3 and 4, complete these exercises in such a way that your answer is as large as possible.

(a)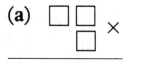

(b)

2 Arrange the digits 2, 4, 7, 8 and 9 in these boxes so as to get the largest possible product.

(a)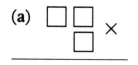

(b)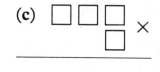

(c)

3 In each of these problems, place any three different digits to make a true statement. How many different solutions can be found in each case?

(a)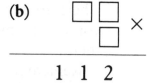

      2 1 6

(b)

      1 1 2

(MR JIG)

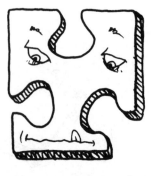

(MR SAW)

Halves and quarters

This is half a shape: 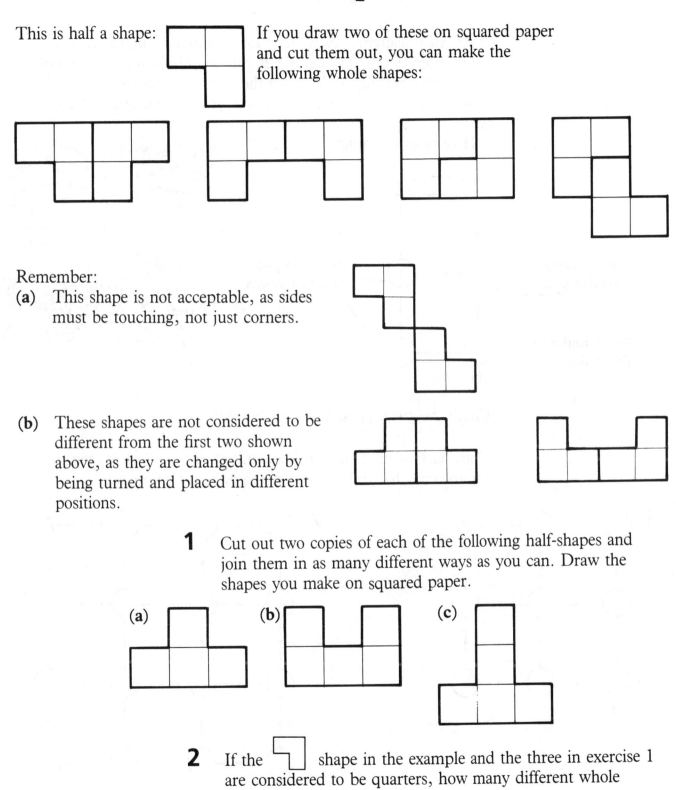 If you draw two of these on squared paper and cut them out, you can make the following whole shapes:

Remember:
(a) This shape is not acceptable, as sides must be touching, not just corners.

(b) These shapes are not considered to be different from the first two shown above, as they are changed only by being turned and placed in different positions.

1 Cut out two copies of each of the following half-shapes and join them in as many different ways as you can. Draw the shapes you make on squared paper.

(a) (b) (c)

2 If the shape in the example and the three in exercise 1 are considered to be quarters, how many different whole shapes can you make?

This time cut out four copies of each one, and don't forget to draw all the whole shapes on squared paper (see page 44).

How many routes?

In the two diagrams below, how many different routes can you follow from A to B in each one if you go only in the direction of the arrows? Starting at A, count the number of different paths by which you can reach each circle, and write the numbers in the circles.

Here is an example:

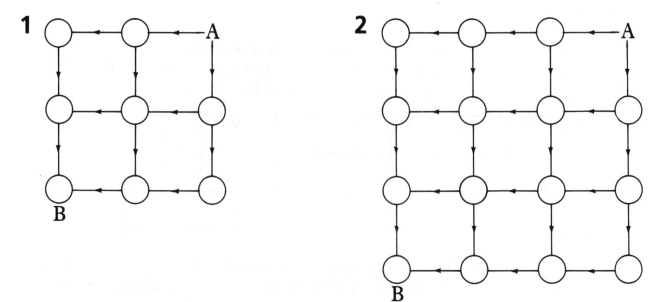

Two paths to this point

Three paths to this point

Only one path to these points

Check the given possible routes carefully.

Copy each of the figures below, and when you have written the numbers in the circles, look for the pattern they make.

1

2

The pattern is called Pascal's triangle although it was used in China before he discovered it. Find out about Pascal's triangle.

Polyiamonds

Polyiamonds are the shapes that are formed when a number of congruent equilateral triangles (triangles all exactly the same shape) are joined together. They were given their name by a Glasgow mathematician, T.H.O'Beirne.

A *diamond* is formed by joining together two equilateral triangles. There is only one diamond.

There is also only one *triamond* — the shape formed by joining together three equilateral triangles.

There are three *tetriamonds*, which are formed by fitting together four equilateral triangles.

To answer the question below, use isometric grid paper (page 46).

Be careful to note shapes which are the same, because each shape can be rotated (turned) or reflected (flipped) so that it looks different. For example, these shapes are the same as the last tetriamond shown above. Do you agree?

  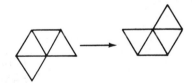

1 A *pentiamond* is formed by joining five equilateral triangles. How many pentiamonds can you find?

2 A *hexiamond* is formed by joining six equilateral triangles. How many hexiamonds can you find?

Strange maths symbols

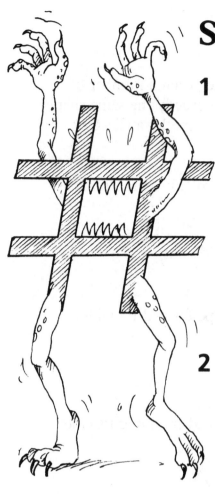

1 The symbol ⋆ placed between two numbers means that you should double the first number and add to the result half the second number.

$$7 \star 4 = 2 \times 7 + \tfrac{1}{2} \times 4 \quad \text{and} \quad 9 \star 2 = 2 \times 9 + \tfrac{1}{2} \times 2$$
$$= 14 + 2 \qquad\qquad\qquad = 18 + 1$$
$$= 16 \qquad\qquad\qquad\quad = 19$$

Find the value of:

(a) $3 \star 6$ **(d)** $10 \star 8$

(b) $5 \star 8$ **(e)** $8 \star 10$

(c) $4 \star 4$ **(f)** $10 \star 10$

2 The symbol ⊙ placed between two numbers means 'square the first number and from your result subtract the second number'.

$$5 \odot 3 = 5^2 - 3 \qquad \text{and} \qquad 4 \odot 7 = 4^2 - 7$$
$$= 25 - 3 \qquad\qquad\qquad\quad = 16 - 7$$
$$= 22 \qquad\qquad\qquad\qquad = 9$$

Find the value of these. In what way is (f) different?

(a) $3 \odot 6$ **(d)** $10 \odot 8$

(b) $5 \odot 8$ **(e)** $8 \odot 10$

(c) $4 \odot 4$ **(f)** $1 \odot 4$

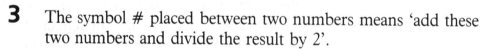

3 The symbol # placed between two numbers means 'add these two numbers and divide the result by 2'.

$$5 \,\#\, 3 = (5 + 3) \div 2 \quad \text{and} \quad 8 \,\#\, 12 = (8 + 12) \div 2$$
$$= 8 \div 2 \qquad\qquad\qquad = 20 \div 2$$
$$= 4 \qquad\qquad\qquad\quad\; = 10$$

Find the value of:

(a) $7 \,\#\, 3$ **(d)** $11 \,\#\, 9$

(b) $3 \,\#\, 7$ **(e)** $21 \,\#\, 7$

(c) $9 \,\#\, 11$ **(f)** $7 \,\#\, 21$

Now try putting these symbols between numbers of your choice. How could you ensure that your answers are always whole numbers?

Problem solving: Act it out

1 Start with a 10p coin. How many other 10p coins can you fit around the outside of it?

   Now repeat this experiment with £1 coins, with 20p coins, with 5p coins and with any other coins. What pattern do you find?

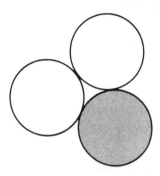

2 Catherine and Fiona receive a total of £25 pocket money each month.
How much does each girl receive if:
(**a**) Catherine has £1 more than Fiona?
(**b**) Catherine has £3 more than Fiona?
(**c**) Catherine has £5 more than Fiona?

3 Ten 1p coins are placed in a row on a desk.
   Every second coin is then replaced with a 5p coin.
   Every third coin is then replaced with a 10p coin.
   Every fourth coin is then replaced with a 20p coin.
   And finally, every fifth coin is replaced with a 50p coin.
What is the value of the ten coins now on the desk?

WHY IS IT SO?

Problem solving: Finding several solutions

1 Using 4 × 4 grid paper or squared paper, show the different ways in which you can place four crosses in a 4 × 4 square so that there is only one cross in any row or column.
Here is one possible way:

			X
		X	
X			
	X		

How many others are there?

2 Here is one way in which three shaded circles can be placed so that they all touch the circumference of the large circle: two touch inside and the third touches outside.
   Draw clear diagrams to illustrate the other possibilities.

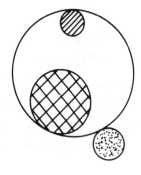

3 Geoffrey's house is 3 km from school, while Effie's house is 2 km from school.
   Draw diagrams showing the possible positions of Effie's house, Geoffrey's house and the school.

Who am I?

To discover who I am, you must eliminate impossibilities.

1 I am the only even prime number.

2 I am the only number that is neither prime nor composite.

3 I am the only two-digit, odd composite number less than 20.

4 I am a two-digit number.
I am a square number.
I am greater than 29.
I am less than 42.

5 I am the sixth prime number.

6 I am a two-digit number.
I am less than 40.
I am exactly divisible by 3 and 10.

7 I am the smallest number exactly divisible by 2, 3 and 4.

8 I am a square number.
I am a two-digit number.
The sum of my digits is 7.
I am divisible by 5.

9 I am greater than 20 and less than 30.
I am even.
I am exactly divisible by 3.

10 I am a two-digit number, less than 25.
I am even.
The sum of my digits is 9.
I am exactly divisible by 3.

11 I am a two-digit number, less than 90 and greater than 45.
I am exactly divisible by 10 and 3.

12 I am a two-digit number.
The sum of my digits is 3.
I am exactly divisible by 5 and 2.

13 I am a two-digit number, less than 25.
I am exactly divisible by 2 and 7.

14 I am a two-digit number, less than 30.
I am exactly divisible by 6 and 8.

Now make up some clues for mystery numbers of your own choice.

Number patterns

The number sentences in each exercise follow a pattern. Find the pattern, continue it for a few more lines, and check your answer on a calculator.

1 $37 \times 3 = 111$
$37 \times 6 = 222$
$37 \times 9 = 333$

2 (a) $91 \times 1 = 91$
$91 \times 2 = 182$
$91 \times 3 = 273$
$91 \times 4 = 364$

(b) $9109 \times 1 = 9109$
$9109 \times 2 = 18\ 218$
$9109 \times 3 = 27\ 327$
$9109 \times 4 = 36\ 436$

3 $143 \times 7 = 1001$
$143 \times 14 = 2002$
$143 \times 21 = 3003$

4 $131 \times 11 = 1441$
$131 \times 111 = 14\ 541$
$131 \times 1111 = 145\ 541$

5 $101 \times 22 = 2222$
$101 \times 222 = 22\ 422$
$101 \times 2222 = 224\ 422$

6 $101 \times 33 = 3333$
$101 \times 333 = 33\ 633$
$101 \times 3333 = 336\ 633$

7 $37 \times 3 = 111$
$37 \times 33 = 1221$
$37 \times 333 = 12\ 321$

8 $1 \times 9 + 2 = 11$
$12 \times 9 + 3 = 111$
$123 \times 9 + 4 = 1111$

9 $9 \times 9 + 7 = 88$
$98 \times 9 + 6 = 888$
$987 \times 9 + 5 = 8888$

10 $1 \times 8 + 1 = 9$
$12 \times 8 + 2 = 98$
$123 \times 8 + 3 = 987$

11 $11^2 = 121$
$111^2 = 12\ 321$
$1111^2 = 1\ 234\ 321$

12 $3367 \times 33 = 111\ 111$
$3367 \times 66 = 222\ 222$
$3367 \times 99 = 333\ 333$

13 $37\ 037 \times 3 = 111\ 111$
$37\ 037 \times 6 = 222\ 222$
$37\ 037 \times 9 = 333\ 333$

14 $999\ 999 \times 2 = 1\ 999\ 998$
$999\ 999 \times 3 = 2\ 999\ 997$
$999\ 999 \times 4 = 3\ 999\ 996$

What is my question?

To solve these problems, you will need to know your tables very well. Study the example before you begin.

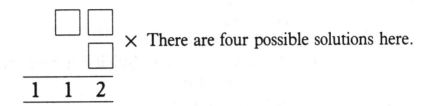 × There are four possible solutions here.

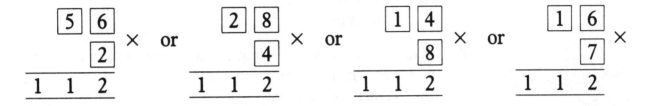

How many different solutions can you find for each of the problems below?

1 □□ ×
      □
    ‾1‾2‾0‾

2 □□ ×
      □
    ‾1‾4‾0‾

3 □□ ×
      □
    ‾1‾5‾0‾

4 □□ ×
      □
    ‾1‾4‾4‾

5 □□ ×
      □
    ‾2‾5‾0‾

6 □□ ×
      □
    ‾1‾3‾2‾

7 □□ ×
      □
    ‾1‾3‾6‾

8 □□ ×
      □
    ‾2‾0‾0‾

Digit puzzles

Using the digits 5 and 6, we can form two 2-digit numbers — 56 and 65 — if the digits cannot be repeated. However, if they can be repeated we can form these numbers:

55	65
56	66

1 Discover how many 2-digit numbers can be formed using 5, 6 and 7 if the digits
(**a**) cannot be repeated;
(**b**) can be repeated.
List all the possibilities.

2 Work out how many 3-digit numbers can be formed using 5, 6 and 7 if the digits
(**a**) cannot be repeated;
(**b**) can be repeated.

3 How many 4-digit numbers can be formed using 5, 6, 7 and 8 if the digits cannot be repeated?

4 (**a**) Luther has to number 27 seats for a concert by sticking the digits 0 to 9 on the back of the seats. Therefore, for seat 23 he will need one digit 2 and one digit 3.
  (i) How many digit 5's will he need?
  (ii) How many digit 2's will he need?
  (iii) How many digit 0's will he need?
(**b**) Luther now has to number 87 seats.
  (i) How many digit 5's will he need?
  (ii) How many digit 2's will he need?
  (iii) How many digit 0's will he need?

_____ _____ _____
(3 LETTERS)

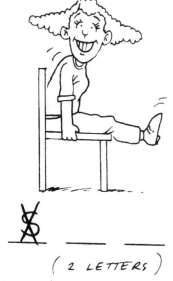

$\not{S}$ _____ _____
(2 LETTERS)

CAN YOU WORK OUT
THIS PUZZLE ?

DIGIT
ANSWER : DIG IT

Make a model, act it out

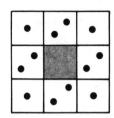

1 This diagram shows how 12 prisoners are arranged in 8 cells, with 4 prisoners in each row of 3 cells. Now arrange 9 prisoners in the 8 cells so that there are 4 in each row of three.

How many different solutions can you find?

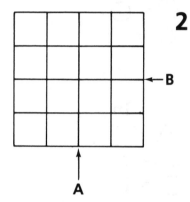

2 Amy is playing with building blocks. She has 4 large blocks ☐ and 4 small blocks ▨ . She places these 8 blocks on the board shown at left in such a way that each row contains one large and one small block and each column contains one large and one small block.

Using squared paper, show how Amy arranges the blocks so that the views (a), (b) and (c), shown below, would be seen if you look in the direction of the arrows.

(a)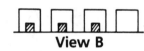

It is recommended that you draw up a large board, like the diagram above, and use blocks or jars.

Then draw your solution on 4 × 4 grid paper from page 45.

(b)

(c)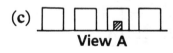

Find my three numbers

In each exercise, I am thinking of three numbers: $\square$, $\triangle$ and $\bigcirc$.
Use the given clues to find my numbers.

1 $\triangle + \triangle + \triangle = 12$
$\triangle + \bigcirc = 7$
$\square + \square = \triangle$
$\triangle + \square + \bigcirc = 9$

2 $\square + \square = 18$
$\square \div \triangle = \triangle$
$\square - \triangle = \bigcirc$
$\triangle + \triangle = \bigcirc$

3 $\triangle + \triangle + \triangle = 18$
$\triangle \div \bigcirc = \square$
$\bigcirc + 1 = \square$
$\triangle - \bigcirc - \square = 1$

4 $\bigcirc + \bigcirc = 16$
$\triangle + \triangle = \bigcirc$
$\square - \triangle = 5$
$\square - \bigcirc = 1$

5 $\square + \square + \square + \square = \triangle + \triangle$
$\triangle - \square = 5$
$\triangle \div \square = 2$
$\triangle + \square + \bigcirc = 18$

6 $\triangle + \bigcirc = 8$
$\triangle - \bigcirc = 4$
$\triangle \div \bigcirc = \square$
$\square + \bigcirc = 5$

7 $\triangle + \square = 13$
$\triangle - \square = 5$
$\square + \bigcirc = 10$
$\bigcirc - \square = 2$

8 $\bigcirc + \square = 13$
$\square + 1 = \bigcirc$
$\triangle + \triangle = \square$
$\bigcirc + \triangle = 10$

9 $\square + \bigcirc = 15$
$\square - \bigcirc = 3$
$\triangle + \triangle = \bigcirc$
$\triangle + \triangle + \triangle = \square$

10 $\triangle + \bigcirc = 12$
$\triangle - \bigcirc = \square$
$\square + \square + 1 = \bigcirc$
$\square + \square + \square + 1 = 7$

Goldbach's conjectures

Goldbach's first conjecture was that 'every even number greater than 4 is the sum of two prime numbers'; for example:

14 = 3 + 11 or 14 = 7 + 7

1   Express the following even numbers as sums of two prime numbers.

    (a) 16   **(c)** 46   **(e)** 92   **(g)** 38
    (b) 24   **(d)** 84   **(f)** 72   **(h)** 98

Goldbach's second conjecture is that 'every odd number greater than 7 is the sum of three prime numbers'; for example:

13 = 5 + 5 + 3 or 13 = 3 + 3 + 7

and for fun we can write the second of these as a diagram, as shown at left.

2   Express each number in these diagrams as the sum of three prime numbers. Under each diagram, write any further solutions you can find.

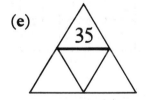
(a)

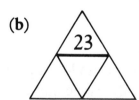
(b)

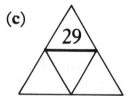
(c)

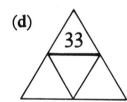
(d)

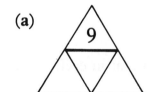
(e)

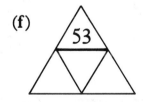
(f)

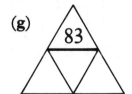
(g)

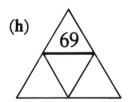
(h)

3   Test Goldbach's conjectures with other numbers. Do you think the conjectures are true?

Domino puzzles

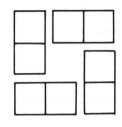

For these problems, you should use the grid paper with blank domino shapes, on page 47.

1 Arrange the four dominoes in each exercise in a hollow square (as shown at left) so that every side is equal to the number given below them.

(a)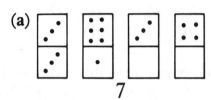
7

(b)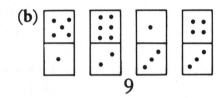
9

(c)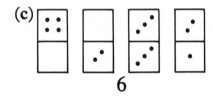
6

(d)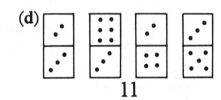
11

(e)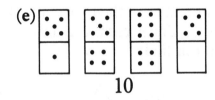
10

2 Arrange these dominoes in hollow squares so that in each exercise all sides equal the same sum.

(a)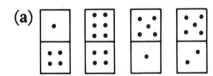

(b)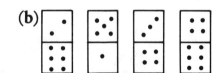

(c)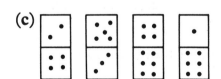

(d)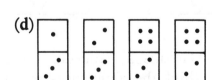

(e)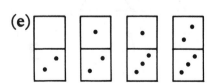

Boat trips

Four friends go on a picnic. They have to cross a river, but there is only one boat for hire and it can hold only three people. How many trips back and forth across the river will be required to move the four to the other side? Remember that the boat cannot return on its own.

Waiting to cross	Crossing or returning	After crossing
4	0	0
1	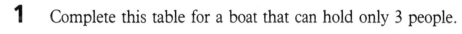 3 →	0
1	← 1	2
0	2 →	2
0	0	4

Draw up a table, as shown. Make a paper boat and use any models to represent the four people. Now act out the problem.

Since one of the first three people to cross must return to pick up the fourth person, if you start with four people, you will have three trips.

1 Complete this table for a boat that can hold only 3 people.

Number of people	Number of trips
1	1
2	1
3	1
4	3
5	
6	
7	
8	
9	
10	
11	
12	

2 Study your table carefully, then write down the number of trips required if:
(a) 20 people go on a picnic;
(b) 22 people go on a picnic.

3 What patterns have you noticed? Explain.

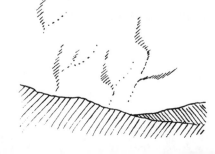

Cake-cutting time

For Jeremy's birthday, his dad made a birthday cake after dinner.

However, first his dad asked Jeremy to make eight round, flat 'cakes' out of modelling clay. Then he asked him to tackle the following challenges, in which he was to divide each cake into a given number of pieces with a given number of cuts, using a fairly blunt knife and straight-line cuts only.

If you cannot use modelling clay, use paper on which blank circles are drawn.

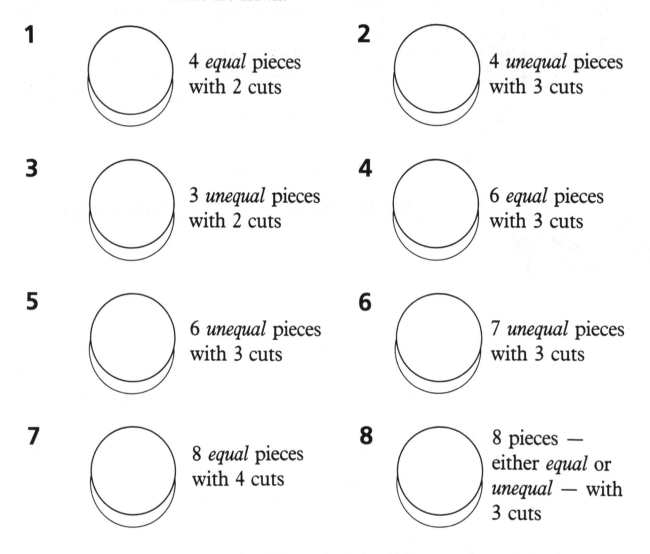

1 4 *equal* pieces with 2 cuts

2 4 *unequal* pieces with 3 cuts

3 3 *unequal* pieces with 2 cuts

4 6 *equal* pieces with 3 cuts

5 6 *unequal* pieces with 3 cuts

6 7 *unequal* pieces with 3 cuts

7 8 *equal* pieces with 4 cuts

8 8 pieces — either *equal* or *unequal* — with 3 cuts

Jeremy's dad promised that if Jeremy mastered the first seven challenges correctly, he would bake a cake for him the next day.

If Jeremy got the last one correct as well, his dad would bake him a cake every day for a week.

Would you have got seven cakes?

The locker problem

In a certain classroom there are 30 lockers numbered 1 to 30. There are also 30 children in the classroom.

One morning, the first child to arrive opens every locker.

The second child to arrive closes all the even-numbered lockers (2, 4, 6 → 30).

The third child goes to the lockers that are multiples of 3 — that is, lockers numbered 3, 6, 9 → 30; of these, this child opens the lockers that are closed, and closes the lockers that are open.

The fourth child goes to lockers 4, 8, 12 → 28 and does the same thing (reverses the state of the lockers). The rest of the 30 children continue this process.

Which lockers are eventually left open?

Locker numbers

Child	1	2	3	4	5	6	7	8	9	10	11	12	13	14	15	16	17	18	19	20	21	22	23	24	25	26	27	28	29	30
1	o	o	o	o	o	o	o	o	o	o	o	o	o	o	o	o	o	o	o	o	o	o	o	o	o	o	o	o	o	o
2		c		c		c		c		c		c		c		c		c		c		c		c		c		c		c
3			c			o			c			o			c			o			c			o			c			o
4				o				o				c				o				o				c				o		
5																														
6																														
7																														
8																														
9																														
10																														
11																														
12																														
13																														
14																														
15																														
16																														
17																														
18																														
19																														
20																														
21																														
22																														
23																														
24																														
25																														
26																														
27																														
28																														
29																														
30																														

Find the correct position

1 Guess the cards.
Four cards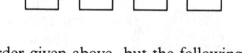

lie face down on the table:

The cards are not in the order given above, but the following facts are known about them:
(a) The card with ★ is to the left of the card with △.
(b) The card with ◯ is not on the edge, and is to the right of the ★.
(c) The card with △ is between the card with ● and the card with ◯.
What is the order of the cards?

2 Here are four views of one cube.

(a) What are the shapes on the faces adjacent to (next to) ☐?
Now work out which shape is on the face opposite ☐.
(b) What are the shapes on the faces adjacent to ⊙? What shape is on the face opposite ⊙?
(c) What shape is on the face opposite ◓?

The four 5's challenge

Insert mathematical signs in the groups of 5's to make each set a true number sentence.

Here is an example: 5 5 5 5 = 1 can be written as:
$(5 + 5 - 5) \div 5 = 1$ or $(5 \div .5) \div (5 \div .5) = 1$

Remember these points:
(a) $\sqrt{5 \times 5} = 5$
(b) $5! = 5 \times 4 \times 3 \times 2 \times 1$
(c) The number 55 may be used.
(d) $5 \div 0.5 = 10$ because there are 10 lots of 0.5 in 5.
(e) The statement $(5 + 5 - 5) \div 5 = 1$ is not considered to be different from $(5 - 5 + 5) \div 5 = 1$.
(f) Do not forget your order of operations:
    Brackets first.
    Multiplication and division next.
    Addition and subtraction last.
(g) Try to find find several solutions for most of the questions.

1	5 5 5 5 = 0	**12**	5 5 5 5 = 26
2	5 5 5 5 = 1	**13**	5 5 5 5 = 30
3	5 5 5 5 = 2	**14**	5 5 5 5 = 45
4	5 5 5 5 = 3	**15**	5 5 5 5 = 50
5	5 5 5 5 = 4	**16**	5 5 5 5 = 55
6	5 5 5 5 = 5	**17**	5 5 5 5 = 75
7	5 5 5 5 = 6	**18**	5 5 5 5 = 100
8	5 5 5 5 = 10	**19**	5 5 5 5 = 120
9	5 5 5 5 = 15	**20**	5 5 5 5 = 125
10	5 5 5 5 = 24	**21**	5 5 5 5 = 130
11	5 5 5 5 = 25	**22**	5 5 5 5 = 150

Make up some of your own.

Stars and shapes

1 Figures are *congruent* if they have the same size and shape.
   Here are three examples of one shape. Can you divide each one into the number of congruent shapes indicated above it?

(a) 2 congruent shapes   **(b)** 3 congruent shapes   **(c)** 4 congruent shapes

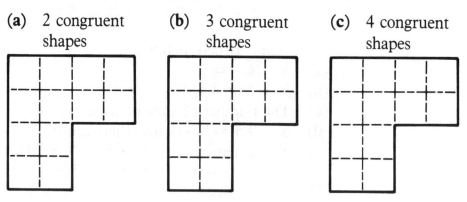

2 Use dot-squared paper (page 48) to do this exercise.
   Three stars have been placed on a 9-dot square grid so that there is only one star in any row or column.

(a) Place 4 stars on a 16-dot square grid so that there is only one star in any row or column. How many different solutions can you find?

(b) Place 4 stars on this 16-dot square grid so that there is no more than one star along any of the lines drawn (including all diagonals).

3 Place only 10 stars in the small squares of this figure in such a way that there is an even number of stars in every row, in every column and in the two diagonals. Use squared paper.

Solutions

Problem solving: guess and check (page 6)

1 Using the numbers 1, 2, 3, 4, 5, 6 and 7, we need to find three number pairs that have the same sum.

(a) If 1 is in the centre : ①2 3 4 5 6 7, the linked pairs each add to 9, so the sum along each line is 10.

(b) If 4 is in the centre: 1 2 3 ④5 6 7, the linked pairs each add to 8, so the sum along each line is 12.

(c) If 7 is in the centre: 1 2 3 4 5 6 ⑦, the linked pairs each add to 7, so the sum along each line is 14.

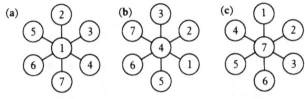

The position of the numbers in the outer circles may vary as long as the pairs are the same as those indicated above.

2 In (a), (b) and (c) the number circled is in the centre of the figure. The number pairs are linked and can be placed on opposite arms of the figure.

(a) ① 2 3 4 5 6 7 8 9 (line total: 12)

(b) 1 2 3 4 ⑤ 6 7 8 9 (line total: 15)

(c) 1 2 3 4 5 6 7 8 ⑨ (line total: 18)

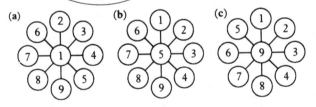

Remember that there are many other possible solutions.

3 The only possible line totals are those given. Children should be encouraged to explain their answer. The solutions for 1 and 2 above suggest why this is so.

What is my message? (page 7)

The order of the problems is not necessarily that in which, as clues, the children will have to use them. Some children may in fact guess the messages and so skip some of the mathematics.

1

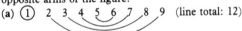

ROCK'N	ROLL	IS	FUN
1 8 3 5 7	1 8 2 2	3 0	6 9 7

$2 \times 2 = 2 + 2$	$3 + 2 = 5$	$5 \div 5 = 1$
$1 \times 1 = 1$	$3^2 = 9$	$2 \times 0 = 0$
$1 + 1 = 2$	$2^2 = 4$	$7 \times 5 = 35$
$3 - 2 = 1$	$2 \times 4 = 8$	$49 \div 7 = 7$
$3 \times 2 = 6$	$6 - 6 = 0$	

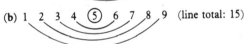

Code:	R	L	C	I	K	F	N	O	U	S
	1	2	3	4	5	6	7	8	9	0

2

MATHS	IS	YUKKY
4 9 1 8 7	3 7	6 2 5 5 6

1837 + 37 = 1874	94 + 94 + 94 = 282	$4 \div 4 = 1$	$6 \times 6 = 36$
		$1 \times 1 = 1$	$1 + 2 = 3$
		$3^2 = 9$	$9 - 5 = 4$
		$2^2 = 4$	$45 \div 5 = 9$
		$5 \times 5 = 25$	$32 \div 8 = 4$

Code:	T	U	I	M	K	Y	S	H	A
	1	2	3	4	5	6	7	8	9

Missing numbers (page 8)

	Number	Rule	Number	Rule	Number	Rule	Number	Rule	Number
1		+8		×2		−10		*÷2	
2		+8		×2		−10		÷2	
3	9		17		34		24		12
4	10		18		36		26		13
5	12		20		40		30		15
6	5		13		26		16		8
7	1		9		18		8		4
8	22		30		60		50		25
9	18		26		52		42		21
10	15		23		46		36		18
11	17		25		50		40		20
12	29		37		74		64		32

* Divide by 2 *or* subtract half.

In exercises 1 and 2, children need to find the rule for each shape. In numbers 3, 4 and 5 they are expected to apply the rule, starting with the first given number. In nos 6–12 they should work backwards as well.

For example, in number 12: 32 was reached by dividing a number by 2, so to find that number by working backwards we must multiply 32 by 2, making the number 64. Again working backwards: 64 was reached by subtracting 10 from a number; to find it we need to add 10 to 64, giving us 74.

Complete the exercise in the same way.

Number squares (page 9)

Guess-and-check will be a very useful strategy here. Suggested starting points are given for exercises 2–5.

1

5	3	4	12
2	4	5	11
1	5	2	8
8	12	11	

A = 3
B = 1
C = 4
D = 5
E = 2

In the second row and the third column C + D = 9, therefore A = 3 (in the first row). Now use trial and error to find the value of C and D: if D = 4 and C = 5, then B = 2, which is impossible, since we know that E = 2. Therefore, D = 5 and C = 4. Alternatively, we could work from the bottom row, where B + D = 6, and then use trial and error.

2

3	1	2	6
4	5	2	11
1	3	4	8
8	9	8	

A = 1
B = 4
C = 5
D = 3
E = 2

Start: C + D = 8 *or* E + D = 5

4

5	1	3	9
4	2	6	12
3	4	2	9
12	7	11	

A = 5
B = 2
C = 6
D = 1
E = 3
F = 4

Start: F + E = 7 *or* D + E = 4

3

4	5	3	12
2	3	1	6
1	4	2	7
7	12	6	

A = 3
B = 5
*C = 1 or 2
*D = 2 or 1
E = 4

*These values can be transposed.

Start: D + C = 3 *or* E + B = 9

5

6	1	3	10
3	2	4	9
2	3	5	10
11	6	12	

A = 3
B = 2
C = 1
D = 6
E = 4
F = 5

Start: B + A = 5 *or* A + F = 8

Completing the lines (page 10)

1 Note that in the shaded lines of each square all the numbers were given, thus providing the magic sums. In (a) and (b), the numbers that should be looked for first are indicated with arrows.

(a) Magic sum: 34

7	6	11	10
14	9	8	3
12	15	2	5
1	4	13	16

(b) Magic sum: 34

8	11	2	13
10	5	16	3
15	4	9	6
1	14	7	12

(c) Magic sum: 42

8	15	14	5
9	11	18	4
12	6	7	17
13	10	3	16

(d) Magic sum: 72

33	5	7	27
11	23	21	17
19	15	13	25
9	29	31	3

(e) Magic sum: 62

23	9	10	20
12	18	17	15
16	14	13	19
11	21	22	8

2 (a)

1	3	5	2	4
5	2	4	1	3
4	1	3	5	2
3	5	2	4	1
2	4	1	3	5

(b)

1	2	3	4	5
3	4	5	1	2
5	1	2	3	4
2	3	4	5	1
4	5	1	2	3

Largest and smallest (page 11)

1
(a) 9 + 8 = 17
(b) 9 + 8 + 7 = 24
(c) 9 + 8 + 7 + 6 = 30
(d) 9 − 1 = 8
(e) 9 + 8 − 1 = 16
(f) 9 − 2 − 1 = 6
(g) 98
(h) 98 + 7 = 105
(i) 98 − 1 = 97
(j) 97 + 86 = 183
(k) 98 − 12 = 86
(l) 98 − 12 − 3 = 83

2
(a) 1 + 2 = 3
(b) 1 + 2 + 3 = 6
(c) 1 + 2 + 3 + 4 = 10
(d) 2 − 1 = 1
  or
  3 − 2
  4 − 3
  5 − 4
  6 − 5
  7 − 6
  8 − 7
  9 − 8
(e) 2 + 1 − 3 = 0
  or
  3 + 1 − 4
  3 + 2 − 5
  4 + 1 − 5
  4 + 2 − 6
  4 + 3 − 7
  5 + 1 − 6
  5 + 2 − 7
  5 + 3 − 8
  5 + 4 − 9
  6 + 1 − 7
  6 + 2 − 8
  6 + 3 − 9
  7 + 1 − 8
  7 + 2 − 9
  8 + 1 − 9
(f) 3 − 1 − 2 = 0
  or
  4 − 1 − 3
  5 − 2 − 3
  6 − 1 − 5
  6 − 2 − 4
  7 − 1 − 6
  7 − 2 − 5
  7 − 3 − 4
  8 − 1 − 7
  8 − 2 − 6
  8 − 3 − 5
  9 − 1 − 8
  9 − 2 − 7
  9 − 3 − 6
  9 − 4 − 5
(g) 12
(h) 12 + 3 = 15
  or
  13 + 2
(i) 12 − 9 = 3
(j) 13 + 24 = 37
  or
  14 + 23
(k) 21 − 19 = 2
  or
  31 − 29
  41 − 39
  51 − 49
  61 − 59
  71 − 69
  81 − 79
(l) 41 − 39 − 2 = 0
  or
  51 − 49 − 2
  61 − 59 − 2
  71 − 69 − 2
  81 − 79 − 2
  or
  51 − 48 − 3
  51 − 43 − 8
  51 − 42 − 9
  61 − 58 − 3
  61 − 57 − 4
  61 − 54 − 7
  61 − 53 − 8
  61 − 52 − 9
  71 − 68 − 3
  71 − 67 − 4
  71 − 63 − 8
  71 − 62 − 9
  81 − 76 − 5
  81 − 75 − 6
  81 − 72 − 9
  or
  45 − 39 − 6
  46 − 39 − 7
  and so on

Multiplying puzzles (page 12)

Children should be encouraged to use calculators to do these puzzles.

1 (a)
$$\begin{array}{r} 32 \\ \underline{\times\ 4} \\ 128 \end{array}$$

(b)
$$\begin{array}{r} 41 \\ \underline{\times\ 32} \\ 1312 \end{array}$$

Children should realise that 4 and 3 must be tens, not units, in order to get the largest product.

2 (a)
$$\begin{array}{r} 87 \\ \underline{\times\ 9} \\ 783 \end{array}$$

(b)
$$\begin{array}{r} 74 \\ \underline{\times\ 92} \\ 6808 \end{array}$$

(c)
$$\begin{array}{r} 874 \\ \underline{\times\ 9} \\ 7866 \end{array}$$

3 (a)

$$\begin{array}{r} 27 \\ 8 \\ \hline 216 \end{array} \times \quad or \quad \begin{array}{r} 24 \\ 9 \\ \hline 216 \end{array} \times \quad or \quad \begin{array}{r} 72 \\ 3 \\ \hline 216 \end{array} \times$$

Note that in these solutions the digits are not different:

$$\begin{array}{r} 54 \\ 4 \\ \hline 216 \end{array} \times \quad \begin{array}{r} 36 \\ 6 \\ \hline 216 \end{array} \times$$

To find all possible solutions, children could write down all the one-digit factors of 216: 2, 3, 4, 6, 8, 9. Now consider all possible combinations of each factor with two other digits to make the given product.

(b)

$$\begin{array}{r} 56 \\ 2 \\ \hline 112 \end{array} \times \quad or \quad \begin{array}{r} 28 \\ 4 \\ \hline 112 \end{array} \times \quad or \quad \begin{array}{r} 14 \\ 8 \\ \hline 112 \end{array} \times \quad or \quad \begin{array}{r} 16 \\ 7 \\ \hline 112 \end{array} \times$$

Halves and quarters (page 13)

In this investigation there are many different shapes to be made; given here are some possible examples. Children should be encouraged to work systematically, using copies of the squared paper on page 44

Check that all versions are in fact different — that is, no 'new' shape is simply an existing one presented in a different position. There should be a thorough discussion with children of which figures (if any) are the same, and why.

1 (a)

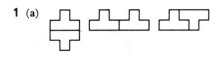

(b)

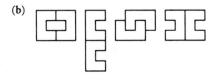

(c)

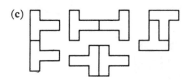

2 Example shape

(a)

(b)

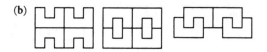

(c)

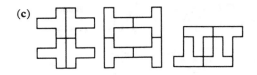

How many routes? (page 14)

1

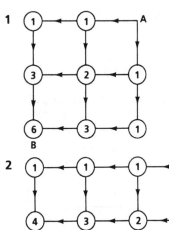

2

Figure 1 is embodied in figure 2.

For each point that has one arrow pointing to it along adjacent arms, there is only one route.

For each point that has two arrows pointing to it ($\downarrow \leftarrow$), the number of routes is the sum of the numbers on the two arms.

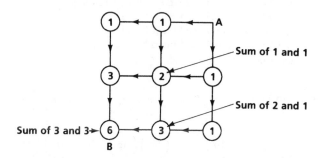

Sum of 1 and 1

Sum of 2 and 1

Sum of 3 and 3 →

Polyiamonds (page 15)

For these exercises, children should be provided with isometric grid paper on page 46.

1 4 pentiamonds

2 12 hexiamonds
Their names were given by T. H. O'Beirne, the Glasgow mathematician who invented the name 'polyiamonds' in 1965.

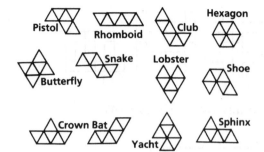

Pistol · Rhomboid · Club · Hexagon
Snake · Lobster · Shoe
Butterfly · Crown Bat · Yacht · Sphinx

Strange maths symbols 1 (page 16)

Children might find it useful to repeat orally the meaning of the relevant symbol as they find the value of each expression.

1 (a) $6 + 3 = 9$
   (b) $10 + 4 = 14$
   (c) $8 + 2 = 10$
   (d) $20 + 4 = 24$
   (e) $16 + 5 = 21$
   (f) $20 + 5 = 25$

2 (a) $9 - 6 = 3$
   (b) $25 - 8 = 17$
   (c) $16 - 4 = 12$
   (d) $100 - 8 = 92$
   (e) $64 - 10 = 54$
   (f) $1 - 16 = -15$

3 (a) $10 \div 2 = 5$
   (b) $10 \div 2 = 5$
   (c) $20 \div 2 = 10$
   (d) $20 \div 2 = 10$
   (e) $28 \div 2 = 14$
   (f) $28 \div 2 = 14$

The symbol * will only produce a whole number if the second number is even. The # needs to have two odds or two even numbers if the result is to be a whole number.

Problem solving: Act it out (page 17)

1 6 coins; given any coin, 6 others of the same value will fit around it exactly.
2 To act out this problem makes it much easier; if we start with £25, in (a) we first give Catherine £1, as she gets £1 more than Fiona, and then share the remaining £24 equally.
  (a) Catherine has £13 and Fiona has £12.
  (b) Catherine has £14 and Fiona has £11.
  (c) Catherine has £15 and Fiona has £10.
3 Total value: £1.77

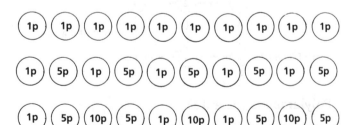

Problem solving: Finding several solutions (page 18)

1 Children should be provided with squared paper or 4×4 grid paper on page 45.

(a)
(b)
(c)

* (d)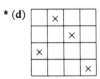
(e)
(f)

* (g)

* Note that square (g) is in fact the same as square (d), since each can be rotated to form the other. Discuss this with the children.

2 7 other possibilities

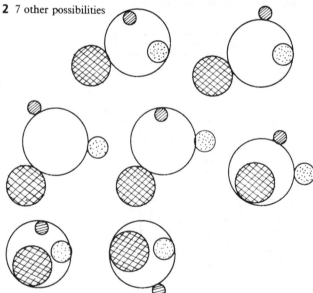

Working systematically is very helpful in this exercise. In the solutions given, the largest of the three was first drawn touching the outside while the smaller circles varied, and then the largest was drawn on the inside.

3

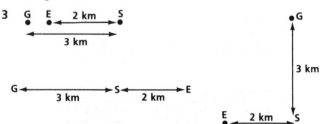

In general

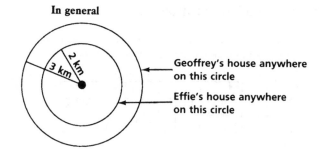

Geoffrey's house anywhere on this circle

Effie's house anywhere on this circle

(Some very bright children will be capable of drawing this diagram.)

Who am I? (page 19)

There are many different ways to solve these conundrums. One possible method is given here for numbers 3 to 14.

1 2

2 1

3 15: List the two-digit numbers less than 20: 10, 11, 12, 13, 14, 15, 16, 17, 18, 19. Now eliminate by crossing out all the numbers which are neither odd nor composite: ~~10, 11, 12, 13, 14,~~ 15, ~~16, 17, 18, 19,~~ and underline the odd composite number: 15.

4 36: This is the only square number greater than 29 and less than 42.

List the square numbers: 1, 4, 9, 16, 25, 36, 49, 64, and eliminate those less than 29 and those greater than 42.

5 13: List the primes and underline the sixth: 2, 3, 5, 7, 11, 13.

6 30: List the two-digit numbers less than 40 and divisible by 10: 10, 20, 30. Now eliminate those not divisible by 3.

7 12: List the numbers divisible by 4: 4, 8, 12, 16
and 3: 3, 6, 9, 12
and 2: 2, 4, 6, 8, 10, 12
until one number occurs in all three cases.

8 25: List the two-digit square numbers: 16, 25, 36, 49, 64, 81; circle ⑯ and ㉕ , in which the sum of the digits is 7, and underline the one that is divisible by 5: 25.

9 24: List the even numbers greater than 20 and less than 30: 22, 24, 26, 28. Now underline the number that is divisible by 3: 24.

10 18: List the even two-digit numbers less than 25: 12, 14, 16, 18, 20, 22, 24. Now underline the number the sum of whose digits is 9: 18. Check that this number is divisible by 3.

11 60: List two-digit numbers greater than 45 and less than 90 that are divisible by 10: 50, 60, 70, 80; underline the number is divisible by 3: 60.

12 30: List the two-digit numbers the sum of whose digits is 3: 12, 21, 30. Now underline the number that is divisible by 5 and 2: 30.

13 14: List the two-digit numbers less than 25 that are divisible by 7: 14, 21. Now underline the number that is also divisible by 2: 14.

14 24: List the two-digit numbers less than 30 that are divisible by 8: 16, 24. Now underline the number that is also divisible by 6: 24.

Number patterns (page 20)

1 $37 \times 12 = 444$
$37 \times 15 = 555$

2 (a) $91 \times 5 = 455$ (b) $9109 \times 5 = 45\ 545$
$91 \times 6 = 546$ $9109 \times 6 = 54\ 654$

3 $143 \times 28 = 4004$
$143 \times 35 = 5005$

4 $131 \times 11\ 111 = 1\ 455\ 541$
$131 \times 111\ 111 = 14\ 555\ 541$

5 $101 \times 22\ 222 = 2\ 244\ 422$
$101 \times 222\ 222 = 22\ 444\ 422$

6 $101 \times 33\ 333 = 3\ 366\ 633$
$101 \times 333\ 333 = 336\ 666\ 633$

7 $37 \times 3333 = 123\ 321$
$37 \times 33\ 333 = 1\ 233\ 321$

8 $1234 \times 9 + 5 = 11\ 111$
$12\ 345 \times 9 + 6 = 111\ 111$

9 $9876 \times 9 + 4 = 88\ 888$
$98\ 765 \times 9 + 3 = 888\ 888$

10 $1234 \times 8 + 4 = 9876$
$12\ 345 \times 8 + 5 = 98\ 765$

11 $11\ 111^2 = 123\ 454\ 321$
$111\ 111^2 = 12\ 345\ 654\ 321$

12 $3367 \times 132 = 444\ 444$
$3367 \times 165 = 555\ 555$

13 $37\ 037 \times 12 = 444\ 444$
$37\ 037 \times 15 = 555\ 555$

14 $999\ 999 \times 5 = 4\ 999\ 995$
$999\ 999 \times 6 = 5\ 999\ 994$

What is my question? (page 21)

1
60×2	30×4	15×8	40×3	20×6	24×5
120	120	120	120	120	120

2
70×2	35×4	20×7	28×5
140	140	140	140

3
75×2	50×3	30×5	25×6
150	150	150	150

4
72×2	36×4	18×8	48×3	24×6	16×9
144	144	144	144	144	144

5 50×5 **6** 66×2 33×4 44×3 22×6
250	132	132	132	132

7 68×2 34×4 17×8 **8** 50×4 25×8 40×5
136	136	136	200	200	200

Digit puzzles (page 22)

1 (a) 6 possibilities
56 or, with a tree
57 diagram:
65
67
75
76

(b) 9 possibilities
55 75
56 76
57 77
65
66
67

2 (a) 6 possibilities

567 or, with a tree
576 diagram:
657
675
756
765

(b) 27 possibilities

555	655	755
556	656	756
557	657	757
565	665	765
566	666	766
567	667	767
575	675	775
576	676	776
577	677	777

3 The first method given is difficult, and should be explained only to the extremely talented student.

☐ ☐ ☐ ☐

1st digit can be chosen in 4 different ways.
2nd digit can be chosen in 3 different ways.
3rd digit can be chosen in 2 different ways.
4th digit can be chosen in 1 way only.
∴ Total number of possibilities = 4 × 3 × 2 × 1
= 24

or

List the possibilities starting with 5:

5678	5768	5867
5687	5786	5876

If we start with 6, 7 or 8, in each case there are again 6 possibilities, and so there is a total of 24.

or

List all 24 possibilities, working systematically.

or

Use a tree diagram:

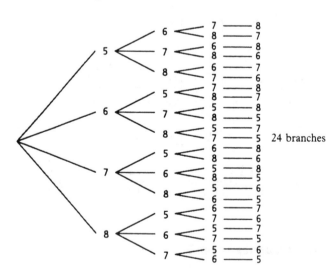

24 branches

4 (a) (i) 2 (for 5 and 15)
(ii) 11 (for 2, 12, 20, 21, 22, 23, 24, 25, 26, 27)
(iii) 2 (for 10 and 20)
(b) (i) 19 (for 5, 15, 25, 35, 45, 50, 51, 52, 53, 54, 55, 56, 57, 58, 59, 65, 75, 85)
(ii) 19 (for 2, 12, 20, 21, 22, 23, 24, 25, 26, 27, 28, 29, 32, 42, 52, 62, 72, 82)
(iii) 8 (for 10, 20, 30, 40, 50, 60, 70, 80)

Make a model, act it out (page 23)

To solve this puzzle, children could be given – or asked to construct — a board and be provided with counters.

1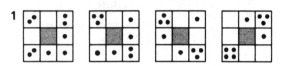

2 To solve these problems, it is helpful to use a model. Children should also be provided with 4 × 4 grid paper (p. 45).

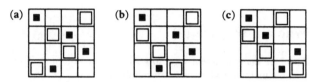

Find my three numbers (page 24)

Logical thinking is needed in answering these questions, and most of them require the children to use guess-and-check strategy as well.

1 △ = 4, ○ = 3, ☐ = 2
Start with the fact that three △s equal 12, so that △ = 4. Now, △ + ○ = 7, so ○ = 3; and since ☐ + ☐ makes 4, ☐ = 2.
2 ☐ = 9, △ = 3, ○ = 6
3 △ = 6, ○ = 2, ☐ = 3
4 ○ = 8, △ = 4, ☐ = 9

5 ☐ = 5, △ = 10, ○ = 3
6 △ = 6, ○ = 2, ☐ = 3
7 △ = 9, ☐ = 4, ○ = 6
8 ○ = 7, ☐ = 6, △ = 3
9 ☐ = 9, ○ = 6, △ = 3
10 △ = 7, ○ = 5, ☐ = 2

Goldbach's conjectures (page 25)

Only some of the possible answers are listed for each exercise.

1 (a) 3 + 13, 5 + 11
(b) 5 + 19, 7 + 17, 11 + 13
(c) 3 + 43, 5 + 41, 17 + 29, 23 + 23
(d) 5 + 79, 11 + 73, 13 + 71, 17 + 67, 23 + 61, 31 + 53, 37 + 47, 41 + 43
(e) 3 + 89, 13 + 79, 19 + 73, 31 + 61
(f) 5 + 67, 11 + 61, 13 + 59, 19 + 53, 29 + 43, 31 + 41
(g) 7 + 31, 19 + 19
(h) 19 + 79, 31 + 67, 37 + 61

2 (a) 9 = 2 + 2 + 5 = 3 + 3 + 3
(b) 23 = 5 + 7 + 11 = 5 + 5 + 13
(c) 29 = 5 + 11 + 13 = 7 + 11 + 11 = 3 + 13 + 13
(d) 33 = 3 + 13 + 17 = 5 + 11 + 17 = 7 + 7 + 19 = 3 + 11 + 19
(e) 35 = 5 + 11 + 19 = 7 + 11 + 17 = 3 + 13 + 19
(f) 53 = 23 + 11 + 19 = 7 + 23 + 23 = 17 + 17 + 19
(g) 83 = 61 + 19 + 3 = 61 + 11 + 11 = 5 + 19 + 59
(h) 69 = 53 + 13 + 3 = 53 + 11 + 5 = 3 + 7 + 59

Domino puzzles (page 26)

Children should be provided with grid paper in empty domino shapes (see p. 47), and should also be given dominoes to work with. They need to act out these problems.

Only one solution is shown for exercises 1(b)–1(e) and exercise 2. There are several other answers when the squares are rotated.

1 (a)

(b) (c) (d) (e)

2 This exercise is quite difficult, as children will have to work out what the sum of each side is to be as well as how to place the dominoes.

(a) (b) (c)

(d) (e)

Boat trips (page 27)

It is advisable for children to act out this problem, using models. It would be very difficult to conceptualise without either doing this or drawing a model (as illustrated for a group of eight people).

Waiting to cross	Crossing or returning	After crossing
8	0	0
5	3 →	0
5	1 ←	2
3	3 →	2
3	1 ←	4
1	3 →	4
1	1 ←	6
0	2 →	6
0	0	8

1 Note the pattern that emerges.

Number of people	Number of trips
1	1
→ 2	1
3	1
→ 4	3
5	3
→ 6	5
7	5
→ 8	7
9	7
→ 10	9
11	9
→ 12	11

2

	People	Trips
(a)	20	19
	21	19
(b)	22	21

3 The pattern for the number of trips is very interesting, as it consists of each odd number repeated. However, when we are looking for patterns we always want to see if we can establish a relationship between the numbers in the first column and the numbers in the second column.

In this case, if the number of people wishing to cross the river is even, the number of trips required is one less than the number of people.

If the number of people is odd, then the number of trips is two less than the number of people.

Cake-cutting time (page 28)

This experiment can be done using pikelets, or modelling clay rolled out flat and cut into circles with an upturned cup or glass.

Alternatively, provide children with copies of sheets on which blank circles have been drawn.

1 2 diameters: all angles at centre are 90°

2 Some possible solutions or or

3 or or

4 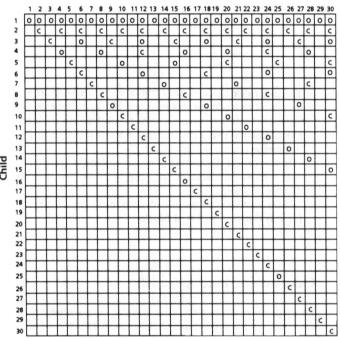 3 diameters: all angles at centre are 60°

5

6

7 4 diameters: all angles at centre are 45°

8 First cut in half , then place one half on top of the other _or_ (if using models) first cut horizontally; then, with pieces stacked, cut as shown

The locker problem (page 29)

Lockers numbered 1, 4, 9, 16 and 25 are open. These locker numbers correspond to square numbers.

Locker numbers

Find the correct position (page 30)

1 ★ ○ △ •

2 Children can either construct the cube by making and cutting out a net of a cube (illustrated at right) or use logic to answer the questions.

   (a) From the first and second views, the shapes on the faces adjacent (next) to □ are ★, ◑, △ and ⊙, so the sixth shape is •

      Therefore, • is opposite □.

   (b) Similarly, from the second, third and fourth views, the shapes adjacent to ⊙ are △, •, □ and ◐. Therefore, the sixth shape, ★, is opposite ⊙.

   (c) △

The four 5's challenge (page 31)

Children must take special care with the order of operations.

   These are some possible solutions. There are many others.

Note: $\sqrt[5]{5^5} \div 5$ (see exercise 2) might seem a very difficult solution to come from such young mathematicians, but in fact it was an answer given to the author by a 10-year-old. ($\sqrt[5]{5^5}$ = the fifth root of 5 to the power of 5. Since $\sqrt{5^2} = 5$, the child concluded the above.)

1 $5 + 5 - 5 - 5 = 0$
$(5 - 5) \times (5 - 5) = 0$
$(5 + 5) \times (5 - 5) = 0$
$(5 \times 5) \times (5 - 5) = 0$
$5 \times (5 - 5) \div 5 = 0$

2 $(5 \div 5) \times (5 \div 5) = 1$
$\sqrt[5]{5^5} \div 5 = 1$

3 $5 \div 5 + 5 \div 5 = 2$
$(\sqrt{5 \times 5} + 5) \div 5 = 2$

4 $(5 + 5 + 5) \div 5 = 3$

5 $(5 \times 5 - 5) \div 5 = 4$
$\sqrt{5 \times 5} - (5 \div 5) = 4$

6 $\sqrt{5 \times 5} + 5 - 5 = 5$
$5 \times 5 \div \sqrt{5 \times 5} = 5$
$\sqrt{5 \times 5} \div .5 - 5 = 5$

7 $\sqrt{5 \times 5} + 5 \div 5 = 6$
$(5 \times 5 + 5) \div 5 = 6$
$55 \div 5 - 5 = 6$

8 $\sqrt{5 \times 5} + \sqrt{5 \times 5} = 10$
$(5 + 5) \times 5 \div 5 = 10$
$(55 - 5) \div 5 = 10$
$5 \div .5 + 5 - 5 = 10$

9 $\sqrt{5 \times 5} + 5 + 5 = 15$
$5 \times 5 - (5 + 5) = 15$
$5 \times 5 - 5 - 5 = 15$
$\sqrt{5 \times 5} \div .5 + 5 = 15$
$5 \div .5 + \sqrt{5} \times \sqrt{5} = 15$

10 $5 \times 5 - (5 \div 5) = 24$

11 $5 \times 5 \times (5 \div 5) = 25$
$5 \times 5 + 5 - 5 = 25$
$\sqrt{5 \times 5} \times \sqrt{5 \times 5} = 25$

12 $5 \times 5 + 5 \div 5 = 26$

13 $5 \times 5 + \sqrt{5 \times 5} = 30$
$5 + 5 \times \sqrt{5 \times 5} = 30$

14 $(5 + 5) \times 5 - 5 = 45$
$5 \times 5 \times .5 - 5 = 45$

15 $5 \times 5 + 5 \times 5 = 50$
$55 - \sqrt{5 \times 5} = 50$
$5! \times .5 - 5 - 5 = 50$

16 $(5 + 5) \times 5 + 5 = 55$
$55 + 5 - 5 = 55$
$55 \times 5 \div 5 = 55$
$5 \times 5 \div .5 + 5 = 55$
$5! \times .5 - \sqrt{5 \times 5} = 55$

17 $(5 + 5 + 5) \times 5 = 75$

18 $(5 \times 5 - 5) \times 5 = 100$
$5! + 5 - (5 \times 5) = 100$

19 $5 \times 5 \times 5 - 5 = 120$
$\sqrt{5 \times 5} - 5 + 5! = 120$

20 $5! + 5 + 5 - 5 = 125$
$5 \times 5 \times \sqrt{5 \times 5} = 125$
$5^5 \div 5 \div 5 = 125$

21 $5 \times 5 \times 5 + 5 = 130$
$5! + 5 + \sqrt{5 \times 5} = 130$

22 $(5 \times 5 + 5) \times 5 = 150$
$5! + 5 \times 5 + 5 = 150$

Stars and shapes (page 32)

Children should be provided with dot-squared paper (p. 48) for exercise 2 and squared paper for exercise 3.

1 (a) (b) (c)
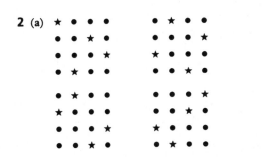

2 (a)
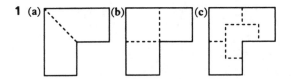

(b)

3

★	★	★	★
		★	★
★		★	
	★	★	

Grid paper and diagram masters

1 cm square paper

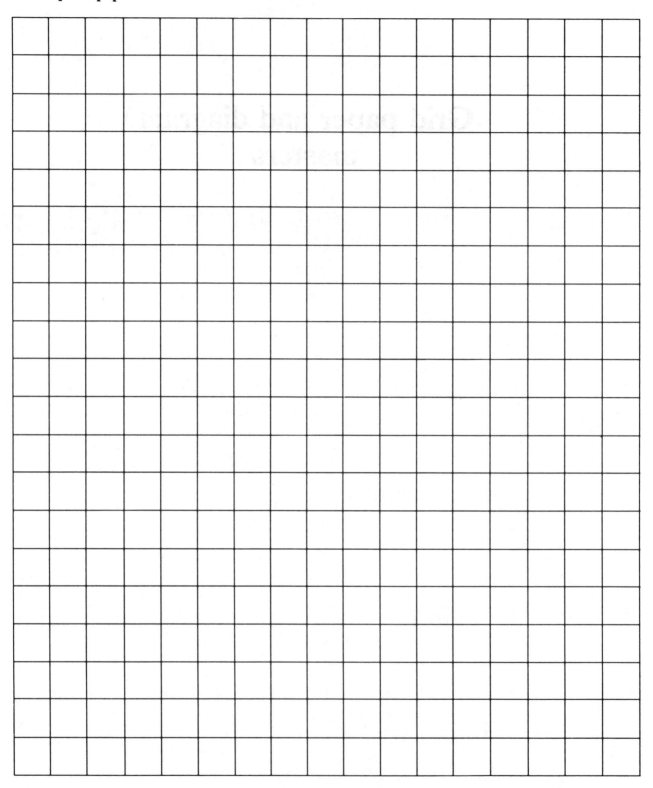

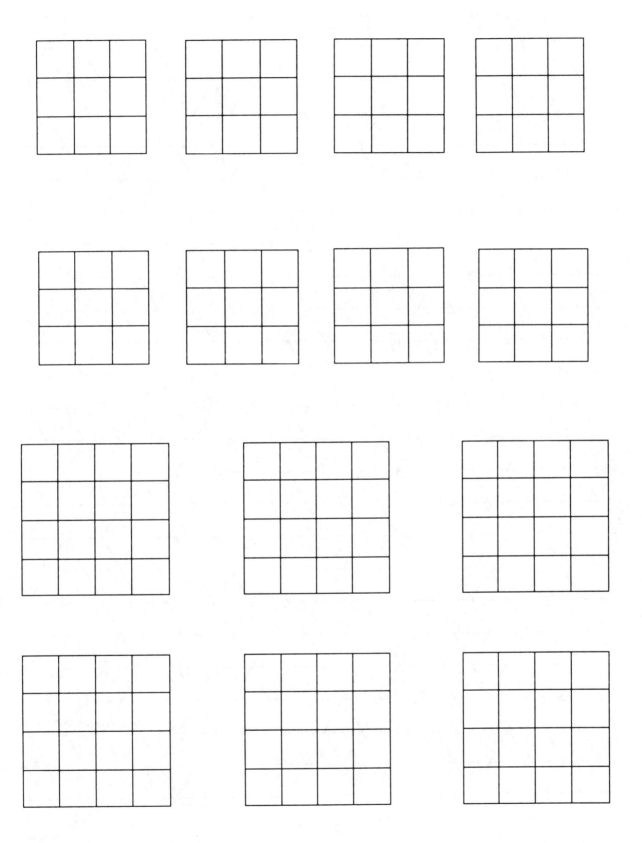

1 cm triangular grid paper

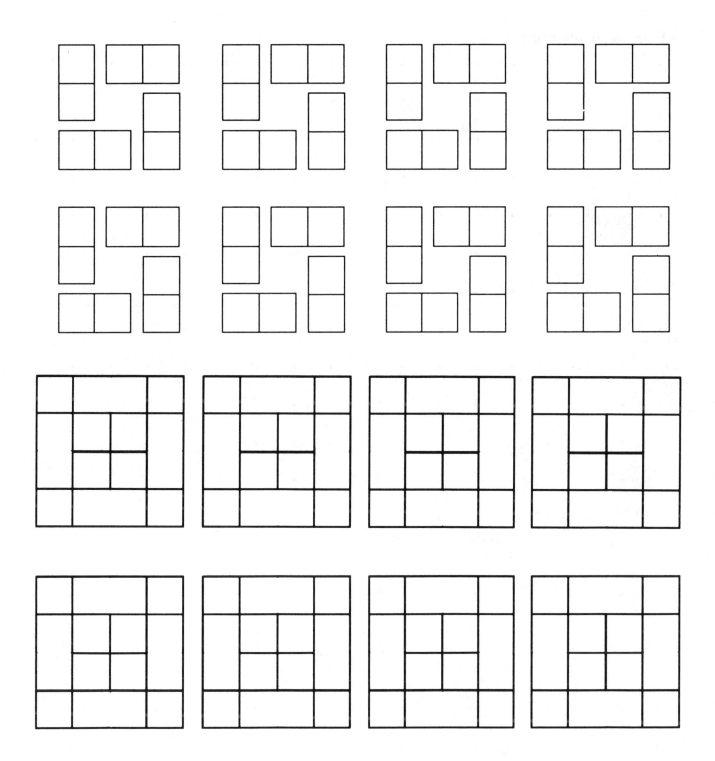

1 cm square dot paper